Nelson
Mathematics 4

Masters Booklet

Series Authors and Senior Consultants
Mary Lou Kestell • Marian Small

Senior Authors
Heather Kelleher • Kathy Kubota-Zarivnij • Pat Milot
Betty Morris • Doug Super

Authors
Carol Brydon • Andrea Dickson • Elizabeth Grill-Donovan
Catharine Gilmour • Jack Hope • Wendy Klassen
David Leach • Pat Margerm • Scott Sincerbox • Rosita Tseng Tam

Assessment Consultant
Damian Cooper

THOMSON
NELSON

Australia   Canada   Mexico   Singapore   Spain   United Kingdom   United States

THOMSON

NELSON

**Nelson Mathematics 4
Masters Booklet**

**Series Authors and
Senior Consultants**
Mary Lou Kestell, Marian Small

Senior Authors
Heather Kelleher,
Kathy Kubota-Zarivnij, Pat Milot,
Betty Morris, Doug Super

Authors
Carol Brydon, Andrea Dickson,
Roz Doctorow, Wendy Dowling,
Catharine Gilmour,
Elizabeth Grill-Donovan,
Jack Hope, Wendy Klassen,
Kathy Kubota-Zarivnij,
David Leach, Pat Margerm,
Gail May, Pat Milot,
Scott Sincerbox, Marian Small,
Mary Steele, Susan Stuart,
Debbie Sturgeon, Rosita Tseng Tam

Assessment Consultant
Damian Cooper

Director of Publishing
David Steele

Publisher, Mathematics
Beverley Buxton

Senior Program Manager
Shirley Barrett

**Teacher's Resource
Program Managers**
Alan Simpson
David Spiegel

Developmental Editors
Janice Barr
Julie Bedford
Jenna Dunlop
James Gladstone
Adrienne Mason
Margaret McClintock
Janice Nixon
Frances Purslow
Elizabeth Salomons
Tom Shields
Alan Simpson
Michael Tabor

Editorial Assistant
Christi Davis

**Executive Managing Editor,
Development & Testing**
Cheryl Turner

**Executive Managing Editor,
Production**
Nicola Balfour

Production Editor
Lu Cormier

Copy Editor
Kathryn Dean

Production Coordinator
Franca Mandarino

Manufacturing Coordinator
Sharon Latta Paterson

Creative Director
Angela Cluer

Art Director
Ken Phipps

Art Management
ArtPlus Ltd., Suzanne Peden

Illustrators
ArtPlus Ltd.

Interior and Cover Design
Suzanne Peden

Cover Image
Corbis/Magna

**ArtPlus Ltd. Production
Coordinator**
Dana Lloyd

Composition
Valerie Bateman/ArtPlus Ltd.

**Photo Research and
Permissions**
Vicki Gould

Printer
Frisby Litho

**National Library of Canada
Cataloguing in Publication**

Nelson mathematics 4.
Teacher's resource /
Mary Lou Kestell ... [et al.].

ISBN 0-17-627235-6

1. Mathematics—Study and
teaching (Elementary)
I. Kestell, Mary Lou
II. Title: Nelson mathematics four.

QA135.6.N444 2003 Suppl. 3
510   C2003-904835-7

Contents

Assessment Masters

Starting-the-Year Review Masters

Multi-Purpose Masters

Initial Assessment Summary

Student: _____ Class: _____ Term: _____

Enter assessment data from Getting Started activities, as well as other initial assessments that you choose.

Date	Chapter	Skills/Concepts	Observations/Next Steps/Intervention

What to Look For When Assessing Student Achievement

When observing students as they work, or when examining completed work, look for the following kinds of evidence.

Problem Solving	Understanding of Concepts	Application of Procedures	Communication
You may focus on one or more of the following steps: • Understand the Problem – assess the learner's depth of understanding of the problem • Make a Plan – assess the learner's choice of an appropriate strategy – assess the completeness of the plan • Carry Out the Plan – assess the effectiveness of the chosen plan – assess the accuracy with which the learner applies procedure(s) and computations in terms of frequency of errors/omissions • Look Back – assess the learner's identification of procedural and computational errors and omissions within a solution – assess the degree to which the learner reflects on the reasonableness of the solution • Communicate – assess the completeness of the learner's explanation of his/her solution – assess the clarity and precision of the explanation – assess the use of mathematical language and representations in the solution	• assess *receptive* communication (i.e., to what extent is it evident that the learner is making the connections that demonstrate he/she "gets it"?) • assess what the learner knows • assess appropriateness and completeness of explanations (i.e., depth of understanding and flexibility in applying that understanding in other contexts) • assess learner's ability to make connections between and among the mathematical ideas and to contexts outside the classroom	• assess the accuracy with which the learner applies procedure(s), in terms of frequency of errors/omissions • assess the appropriate use of procedures	• assess *expressive* communication (i.e., to what extent is the learner's communication clear and precise to the reader?) • assess what the learner records about what he/she knows • assess clarity and precision of descriptions, explanations, and justifications • assess logical flow and organization of ideas • assess correct and effective use of mathematical language and conventions

Coaching Students Towards Success

Use the following prompts when providing students with feedback to help them improve their learning.

Problem Solving	Understanding of Concepts	Application of Procedures	Communication
• Check using a calculator. • What information is given? What information is important? What information is not important? • What are you asked to find out? • What do you need to know? • What information is important to solve this problem? • What information is missing? • How is this problem similar to/different from ones you have done before? What strategies could help you? • Show your mathematical thinking at every stage (Understand, Plan, Do, Look Back, Communicate). • Show the materials and representations that helped you solve the problem. • Use different ways to show what you did. • Justify your answer. Tell what you were thinking. • How do you know you are right? (reasonableness – Look Back)	• "Ink your thinking" • Talk me through what you did • Make it short but say enough that I can see what you were thinking • Explain with more detail • Describe the math idea; explain how the idea relates to another math idea; provide an example to explain the idea	• Calculate, draw, construct, manipulate, measure, count, tell time, estimate • Check by doing it backwards (inverse operations) • Check the reasonableness by estimation	• Read over what you have written. • Does it make sense? • Do you need to explain more fully? • Have you used precise, correct mathematical terms? • Have you used correct mathematical terms and/or symbols?

Conducting In-Class Student Interviews

Nelson Mathematics stresses the importance of *assessment for feedback* as the key to helping students improve their learning. Furthermore, many students can reveal far more about what they do and do not understand in mathematics if they have opportunities to *talk*, one-on-one, with the teacher on a regular basis. Clearly, lack of time and large class sizes make the scheduling of such interviews problematic. However, by using a structured approach such as the one outlined below, teachers can be sure that students having difficulty are identified early, that no students "slip through the cracks," and that every student has had several opportunities for one-on-one contact before the first report card goes home.

Here are some suggested tips on how to build one-on-one interviews into your mathematics program:

- Establish specific times during the term when you will conduct interviews. It is suggested that interviews will be most beneficial to students if they coincide with the *Mid-Chapter* and *End-of-Chapter Reviews*.

- Set up a schedule that allows you to interview five to eight students during each session.

- Inform the group of students who will be interviewed the next day so they will be prepared.

- Assign the rest of the class engaging, quiet work to minimize interruptions.

- Create a large poster that clearly describes your behavioural expectations for the rest of the class during interview time. (For suggestions about what to include, refer to the indicators for "Independent Work" that appear in the *Guide to the Provincial Report Card*, Ontario 1998.)

- Time each interview to be no longer than seven minutes. If a particular student needs more time, he/she may return once the other students scheduled for that day have had their interviews.

- Take the time to teach students about your behavioural expectations, both for those being interviewed and for the rest of the class.

- Use one of the Student Interview forms to keep track of each interview.

- Refer to your interview notes when talking to parents.

Student Interview Form (with prompts)

It is suggested that you use questions and tasks from the Mid-Chapter Review or End-of-Chapter Review as the context for interviewing students. Additional bullets are provided for your own prompts.

Name: _____

Problem Solving *(Focus on selection and use of appropriate strategies.)*

Sample prompts:
- What are you asked? _____
- What information is important? _____
- What strategy did you use? _____
- Show me what you did. _____
- How do you know if it's right? _____
- _____

Understanding of Concepts *(Focus on the question "Does the student understand?")*

Sample prompts:
- Can you explain to me…? _____
- How is….like….? _____
- Talk me through what you did. _____
- _____
- _____
- _____

Application of Procedures *(Focus on accuracy in a variety of contexts.)*

Sample prompts:
- Calculate… _____
- Measure… _____
- Estimate… _____
- Check… _____
- _____
- _____

Communication *(Focus on clarity and precision.)*

Sample prompts:
- Is your explanation easy for others to understand? _____
- Have you used terms and symbols correctly? _____
- _____

Observations/Next Steps/Intervention _____
_____
_____

Student Interview Form (without prompts)

It is suggested that you use questions and tasks from the Mid-Chapter Review or End-of-Chapter Review as the context for interviewing students.

Name: _____

Problem Solving *(Focus on selection and use of appropriate strategies.)*

_____
_____
_____
_____
_____
_____
_____

Understanding of Concepts *(Focus on the question "Does the student understand?")*

_____
_____
_____
_____
_____
_____
_____

Application of Procedures *(Focus on accuracy in a variety of contexts.)*

_____
_____
_____
_____
_____
_____
_____

Communication *(Focus on clarity and precision.)*

_____
_____
_____
_____
_____
_____
_____

Observations/Next Steps/Intervention _____
_____
_____

Problem Solving Rubric

- This is a generic assessment tool. Not all criteria are necessarily appropriate to a given task.
- Remember that problem solving is not a linear process; skilled problem solvers move back and forth between the steps.
- This rubric may be used to observe students as they are working on a problem, or it may be used to assess completed work.
- Level 1 represents a limited performance but one in which the student has engaged with the prescribed task to some extent. Some students will perform below Level 1.

Criteria	Level 1 – Very Limited	Level 2 – Developing	Level 3 – At Standard	Level 4 – Exceeds Standard
Think: Understand the Problem	• Shows insufficient understanding of the problem (i.e., is unable to identify sufficient information or to restate problem)	• Shows partial understanding of the problem (i.e., is able to identify some of the relevant information but has difficulty restating problem)	• Shows complete understanding of the problem (i.e., is able to identify relevant information and to restate problem)	• Shows in-depth understanding of the problem (i.e., is able to differentiate between relevant and irrelevant information and is able to rephrase problem)
Plan: Make a Plan	• Shows little or no evidence of a plan	• Shows evidence of a partial plan	• Shows evidence of an appropriate plan	• Shows evidence of a thorough plan
Do: Carry Out the Plan	• Uses a strategy and attempts to solve problem but does not arrive at an answer • Use of procedures includes major errors and/or omissions	• Carries out the plan to some extent, using a strategy, and develops a partial and/or incorrect solution • Use of procedures includes several errors and/or omissions	• Carries out the plan effectively by using an appropriate strategy and solving the problem • Use of procedures is mostly correct, but there may be a few minor errors and/or omissions	• Shows flexibility and insight when carrying out the plan by trying and adapting one or more strategies to solve the problem • Use of procedures includes almost no errors or omissions
Look Back: Review Solution	• Is unable to identify either errors or omissions in the plan or in the attempted solution	• Has some difficulty checking plan and attempted solution for errors and/or omissions	• Checks the plan and solution for procedural errors and omissions	• Thoroughly reviews the plan and solution for effectiveness of strategies chosen and for procedural errors and omissions • Verifies the answer and judges whether it is reasonable
Communicate (For more depth, see the full Communication Rubric–Assessment Tool 10.)	• Provides an incomplete explanation of the strategy/solution that lacks clarity (i.e., uses very little mathematical language; makes very little use of mathematical representations—models, diagrams, graphs, tables)	• Provides a partial explanation of the strategy/solution that shows some clarity (i.e., uses some mathematical language correctly; makes some use of mathematical representations—models, diagrams, graphs, tables—as required/as necessary)	• Provides a complete and clear explanation of the strategy/solution (i.e., uses mathematical language correctly; makes appropriate use of mathematical representations—models, diagrams, graphs, tables—as required/as necessary)	• Provides a thorough, clear, and insightful explanation of the strategy/solution (i.e., uses precise mathematical language; makes most appropriate use of mathematical representations—models, diagrams, graphs, tables—as required/as necessary)

Understanding of Concepts Rubric

- *This is a generic assessment tool. Not all criteria are necessarily appropriate to a given task.*
- *This rubric is well suited to assessing understanding orally in a teacher-student conference or when assessing journal responses.*
- *Level 1 represents a limited performance but one in which the student has engaged with the prescribed task to some extent. Some students will perform below Level 1.*

Criteria	Level 1 – Very Limited	Level 2 – Developing	Level 3 – At Standard	Level 4 – Exceeds Standard
Depth of Understanding	• Demonstrates a superficial or inaccurate understanding of concept(s) (i.e., restates what was taught but with inaccuracies)	• Demonstrates a growing but still incomplete understanding of concept(s) (i.e., provides incomplete explanation of thinking)	• Demonstrates grade-appropriate understanding of concept(s) (i.e., provides appropriate and complete explanation of thinking)	• Demonstrates in-depth understanding of concept(s) (i.e., provides clear, complete, and logical explanation that may go beyond what was taught)
Making Connections	• Has difficulty connecting new concept(s) to prior learning • Makes very simple connections between concepts when provided with a highly structured approach	• Demonstrates a limited ability to connect new concept(s) to prior learning • Makes simple connections between concepts in familiar or simple contexts (i.e., relies on a limited set of routines)	• Demonstrates a growing ability to connect new concept(s) to prior learning • Makes connections between concepts in new contexts (i.e., shows a growing ability to think flexibly)	• Easily connects new concept(s) to prior learning • Makes connections between concepts in new and unfamiliar contexts (i.e., shows flexible and adaptive thinking)
Reflective Thinking (Metacognition)	• Makes very simple observations about completed work and/or new learning (e.g., in a teacher-student conference or a journal)	• Makes simple observations about completed work and/or new learning (e.g., in a teacher-student conference or a journal)	• Makes grade-appropriate observations about completed work and/or new learning to clarify thinking and increase understanding (e.g., in a teacher-student conference or a journal)	• Makes insightful observations about completed work and/or new learning to clarify thinking and increase understanding (e.g., in a teacher-student conference or a journal)

Application of Procedures Rubric

- *This is a generic assessment tool. Not all criteria are necessarily appropriate to a given task.*
- *This rubric may be used to observe students as they are working, or it may be used to assess completed work.*
- *Level 1 represents a limited performance but one in which the student has engaged with the prescribed task to some extent. Some students will perform below Level 1.*

Criteria	Level 1 – Very Limited	Level 2 – Developing	Level 3 – At Standard	Level 4 – Exceeds Standard
Selection of Procedures	• Selects an inappropriate procedure for a given task or simple word problem	• Selects a simple or partially appropriate procedure for a given task or simple word problem	• Selects an appropriate procedure for a given task or simple word problem	• Selects the most efficient procedure for a given task or simple word problem or identifies own procedure
Application of Procedures	• Makes major errors and/or omissions when applying procedure(s) • Has difficulty following appropriate sequence for a given procedure	• Makes several errors and/or omissions when applying procedure(s) • Makes some errors in sequencing for a given procedure	• Makes only a few minor errors and/or omissions when applying procedure(s) • Follows an appropriate sequence for a given procedure	• Makes almost no errors when applying procedure(s) • Follows most appropriate sequence for a given procedure

Communication Rubric

Expressive Communication: Speaking, Writing, and Representation

- *This is a generic assessment tool. Not all criteria are necessarily appropriate to a given task.*
- *This rubric should be used to assess the degree to which students are able to communicate about their understanding of concepts, procedures, and problem solving strategies. Use only those criteria that are appropriate to a given task.*
- *Level 1 represents a limited performance but one in which the student has engaged with the prescribed task to some extent. Some students will perform below Level 1.*

Criteria	Level 1 – Very Limited	Level 2 – Developing	Level 3 – At Standard	Level 4 –, Exceeds Standard
Explanation and justification of mathematical concepts, procedures, and problem solving	• Provides incomplete or inaccurate explanations/justifications that lack clarity or logical thought, using minimal words, pictures, symbols, and/or numbers	• Provides partial explanations/ justifications that exhibit some clarity and logical thought, using simple words, pictures, symbols, and/or numbers	• Provides complete, clear, and logical explanations/justifications, using appropriate words, pictures, symbols, and/or numbers	• Provides thorough, clear, and insightful explanations/justifications, using a range of words, pictures, symbols, and/or numbers
Organization of material (written, spoken, or drawn)	• Organization is minimal and seriously impedes communication	• Organization is limited but does not seriously impede communication	• Organization is sufficient to support communication	• Organization is effective and aids communication
Use of mathematical vocabulary	• Uses very little mathematical vocabulary, and vocabulary used lacks clarity and precision	• Uses a limited range of mathematical vocabulary with some degree of clarity and precision	• Uses mathematical vocabulary with sufficient clarity and precision to communicate ideas	• Uses a broad range of mathematical vocabulary to communicate clearly and precisely
Use of mathematical representations (graphs, charts, diagrams)	• Uses representations that exhibit minimal clarity and accuracy and are ineffective in communicating	• Uses representations that lack clarity and accuracy, though not sufficient to impede communication	• Uses representations that are sufficiently clear and accurate to communicate	• Uses representations that are clear, precise, and effective in communicating
Use of mathematical conventions (units, symbols, labels)	• Few conventions are used correctly	• Some conventions are used correctly	• Most conventions are used correctly	• Almost all conventions are used correctly

Using the Assessment of Learning Summary—Individual Student

The Assessment of Learning Summary *is used to generate the student's report card grade. For this reason, it should include no data from* Initial Assessment *or* Assessment for Feedback *tasks.*

1. Use this chart to record all assessment data that will be used to generate a student's report card grade. This will include assessments you have designed, as well as assessments from *Nelson Mathematics*.

2. You may enter numerical marks, rubric levels, and/or letter grades on the chart.

3. Enter all required information on the chart as follows:
   - enter the date and assessment task under the appropriate category, for example, *Sept. 10; Pattern Block Puzzle* under Problem Solving
   - enter the mark (score, level, or letter grade) in the appropriate row
   - make anecdotal comments about both student achievement in the curriculum and learning skills in the Strengths, Areas for Improvement, and Next Steps box

4. As a reporting period approaches, you will need to summarize each student's achievement according to his/her most consistent level of performance for each category and then for the whole strand. To help you do this, you will need
   - the Assessment Rubrics for *Problem Solving, Understanding of Concepts, Application of Procedures,* and *Communication* (Assessment Tools 7–10)

5. For a given category (e.g., Problem Solving):
   - review the student's marks, for example, 3, 6/10, 3−, 2+, 14/20, 3
   - refer to the *Problem Solving Rubric* and ask the question, "Which set of indicators best characterizes this particular student's achievement at this time?"
   - enter the corresponding level in the Most Consistent Level column, for example, Level 3 for the marks listed in the first bullet
   - repeat this process for the other three categories

6. To determine the most consistent level across a whole strand such as Patterning and Algebra, look at the most consistent level for each category. Then determine the most consistent level overall.

Assessment of Learning Summary–Individual Student

Assessment Tool 10

Student: _____   Class: _____   Term: _____

Choose either Tool 12 or Tool 14 to record summary achievement data

Category	Problem Solving	Most Consistent Level	Understanding of Concepts	Most Consistent Level	Application of Procedures	Most Consistent Level	Communication	Most Consistent Level	Most Consistent Level Across Strand
Assessment Task Date									
Number Sense and Numeration									
Measurement									
Geometry and Spatial Sense									
Patterning and Algebra									
Data Management and Probability									

Comments:
Strengths,
Areas for
Improvement,
and Next Steps

Using the Assessment of Learning Summary—Class by Strand

The Assessment of Learning Summary *is used to generate students' report card grades. For this reason, it should include no data from* Initial Assessment *or* Assessment for Feedback *tasks.*

1. Use this chart to record all assessment data that will be used to generate students' report card grades for a given strand. This will include assessments you have designed, as well as assessments from *Nelson Mathematics*. You will need three more charts for each of the other strands.

2. You may enter numerical marks, rubric levels, and/or letter grades on the chart.

3. Enter all required information on the chart as follows:
   - enter the assessment task and date in the top row, for example, *Describing Patterns, Sept. 10*
   - check which category is being assessed (Problem Solving, Understanding of Concepts, Application of Mathematical Procedures, or Communication)
   - enter the mark for each student (score, level, or letter grade) in the appropriate row

4. As a reporting period approaches, you will need to summarize each student's achievement according to his/her most consistent level of performance for the whole strand. To help you do this, you will need:
   - the Assessment Rubrics for *Problem Solving, Understanding of Concepts, Application of Mathematical Procedures*, and *Communication* (Assessment Tools 7–10)

5. To determine the most consistent level across a whole strand such as Patterning and Algebra, you will need to:
   - review the student's marks, for example, 3, 6/10, 3−, 2+, 14/20, 3
   - refer to the four Assessment Rubrics (Assessment Tools 7–10) and ask the question, "Which set of indicators best summarizes this particular student's achievement at this time?"
   - enter the corresponding level in the Most Consistent Level column, for example, Level 3, for the set of marks listed in the first bullet above.

Assessment of Learning Summary—Class by Strand

Class: _____   Strand: _____   Year: _____

PS – Problem Solving
UC – Understanding of Concepts
AP – Application of Procedures
C – Communication

Choose either Tool 12 or Tool 14 to record summary achievement data.

Lesson: Task: Date:									Most Consistent Level
Check (✔) **Category**	PS/UC/AP/C	PS/UC/AP/C	PS/UC/AP/C	PS/UC/AP/C	PS/UC/AP/C	PS/UC/AP/C	PS/UC/AP/C	PS/UC/AP/C	PS/UC/AP/C
Student									

Using the Assessment of Learning Skills Chart

1. Use this chart throughout the term to record your observations about students' learning skills. Then use the chart to summarize learning skills data for the report card.

2. Aim to have 3 observations of each student for each learning skill before a reporting period occurs.

3. Observe only a portion of the class on any given day. Select only the learning skill or skills that are evident during that day's work. For example, when students are working together on solving a rich problem, you will likely be able to assess *Initiative, Use of Information,* and *Co-operation.*

4. Aim to spread your observations over the course of the term to allow students the opportunity to improve their skills over time.

5. When determining *Most Consistent Level* for the report card, use your professional judgement in ways that encourage students to improve. For example, if you had observed Sukan's level of *Co-operation* on three separate occasions as *N, N,* and *G,* you may wish to summarize this as *G* in order to recognize her recent improvement.

6. Since learning skills appear as a summary for all subjects on the report card, teachers of different subjects need to reach consensus with respect to each student's *Most Consistent Level* of performance. This can be achieved by having the core teacher summarize the learning skills data for each student, and then having teachers of other subjects review the summaries to see if they correspond with their own assessments.

7. Refer to the *Guide to the Provincial Report Card, Grades 1–8, Appendix D* for detailed descriptions of each of the nine learning skills. It is strongly suggested that these descriptions be shared with students so they know what behaviours are expected with respect to each learning skill.

Assessment of Learning Skills Chart

Assessment Tool 12

E Excellent
G Good
S Satisfactory
N Needs Improvement

Class: _____   Term: *Fall*

Learning Skill:	Independent Work			Initiative			Homework Completion			Use of Information			Co-operation			Conflict Resolution			Class Participation			Problem Solving			Goal Setting			Most Consistent Level (for each learning skill)								
Date: (month)	9	9	10	9	10	10	9	9	10	9	10	10	9	10	11	9	10	11	9	9	10	9	10	11	9	10	11	IW	IN	HC	UI	CO	CR	CP	PS	GS
Students																																				
Sukan	G	G		N	S		S	S		S	G	G	N	G		N	S		S	G		S	S	S	N	N		G	N	S	G	G	G	S	S	N

Assessment of Learning Skills Chart

Assessment Tool 12

Class: _____

Term: _____

E   Excellent
G   Good
S   Satisfactory
N   Needs Improvement

Learning Skill:	Independent Work	Initiative	Homework Completion	Use of Information	Co-operation	Conflict Resolution	Class Participation	Problem Solving	Goal Setting	Most Consistent Level (for each learning skill)								
Date: (month)										IW	IN	HC	UI	CO	CR	CP	PS	GS
Students																		

Crossnumber Puzzle

Use the clues to complete the crossnumber puzzle.
Write one digit in each square.

Across

A. 2 hundreds, 5 tens, 6 ones
C. one less than 100
D. 3 hundreds
E. 6 hundreds, 3 tens, 2 ones
H. 5 hundreds, 6 ones
J. 5 hundreds, 7 tens, 6 ones
L. 7 hundreds, 8 tens, 1 one
O. 1 hundred, 8 tens
P. 3 hundreds, 9 ones
Q. 3 hundreds, 7 tens, 3 ones
S. 4 hundreds, 7 tens, 3 ones
U. seventy-six
V. 9 hundreds, 8 tens, 1 one

Down

A. 2 hundreds, 4 tens
B. 600 + 60 + 6
C. ninety-two
D. 3 hundreds, 9 tens, 5 ones
F. 3 hundreds, 9 tens, 7 ones
G. seventy
H. fifty-one
I. 6 hundreds, 7 tens, 8 ones
K. 700 + 20 + 3
M. 800 + 10 + 6
N. 4 hundreds, 9 tens, 3 ones
O. 1 hundred, 2 tens, 7 ones
R. 7 hundreds, 5 tens, 9 ones
S. 4 tens, 5 ones
T. 3 hundreds, 7 tens, 2 ones

Name: _____ Date: _____

Numeration Practice

Use a ruler to connect numbers that are the same.

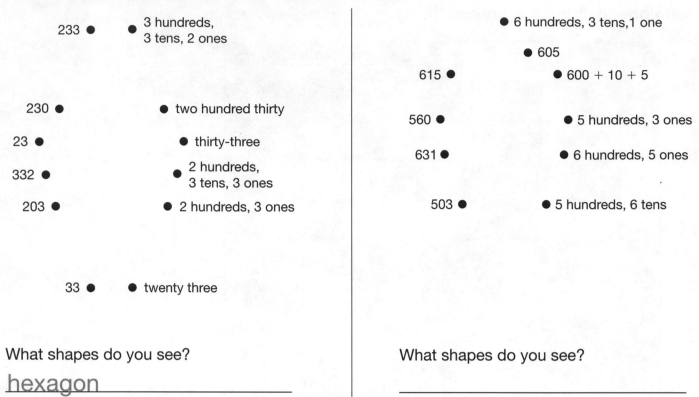

233 ●   ● 3 hundreds, 3 tens, 2 ones

230 ●   ● two hundred thirty

23 ●   ● thirty-three

332 ●   ● 2 hundreds, 3 tens, 3 ones

203 ●   ● 2 hundreds, 3 ones

33 ●   ● twenty three

● 6 hundreds, 3 tens, 1 one

● 605

615 ●   ● 600 + 10 + 5

560 ●   ● 5 hundreds, 3 ones

631 ●   ● 6 hundreds, 5 ones

503 ●   ● 5 hundreds, 6 tens

What shapes do you see?

hexagon _____

What shapes do you see?

_____

Use a ruler to connect the numbers in order.

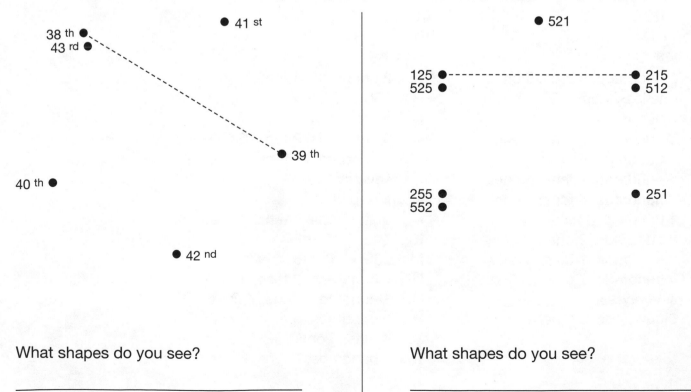

● 41 st

38 th ●
43 rd ●

39 th ●

40 th ●

42 nd ●

● 521

125 ●- - - - - - - - - - -● 215
525 ●   ● 512

255 ●   ● 251
552 ●

What shapes do you see?

_____

What shapes do you see?

_____

Name: _____ Date: _____

Operations Practice

Help the hungry bee find the flowers.
The path to the flowers follows the answers that end in 8.
The bee can move only like this: ↑ ↓ ← → .

85 − 37	356 + 422	12 + 16	19 + 39	30 + 8	74 + 94	159 + 389	160 + 388
29 − 1	49 + 29	79 − 29	79 − 21	50 − 2	74 + 96	130 − 12	130 − 18
36 + 12	598 − 230	100 − 52	14 − 8	28 + 4	3 × 4	29 + 9	4 × 4
36 − 12	598 + 2	14 − 6	18 − 8		9 × 2	30 − 2	16 ÷ 4
15 − 7	16 − 8	95 − 7	95 − 8	33 − 15	8 × 2	5 × 2	4 × 8
49 + 21	49 − 21	49 − 21	523 − 116	928 − 36	8 × 4	16 ÷ 2	2 × 4
25 + 3	365 + 413	141 + 7	338 − 330	925 − 417	43 − 25	7 × 4	16 ÷ 8

Name: _____ Date: _____

Addition and Subtraction Practice

Colour each section that has an answer

- **less than 20—blue.**
- **between 20 and 50—yellow.**
- **between 50 and 100—green.**
- **between 100 and 200—red.**
- **greater than 200—purple.**

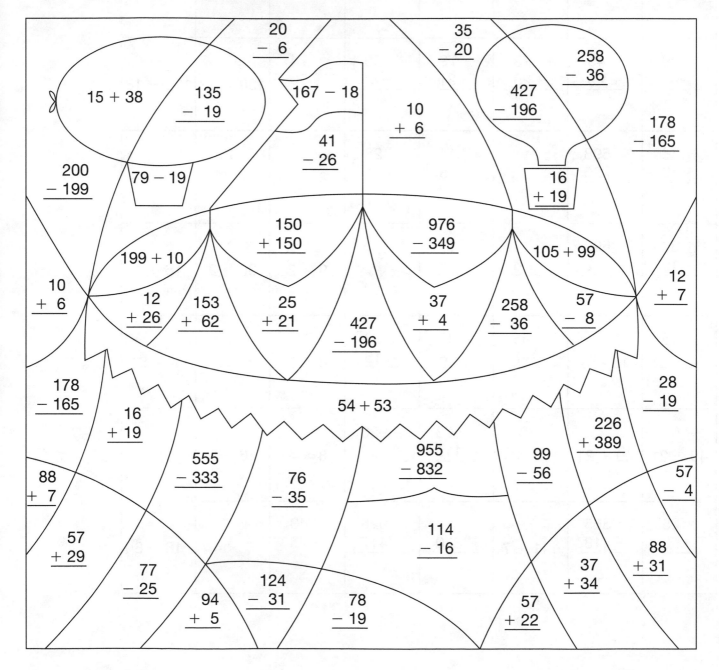

Subtraction Practice

Cut out the triangles.

Move them around to complete the subtraction sentences.

Hint: The correct answer will make a shape with 4 sides.

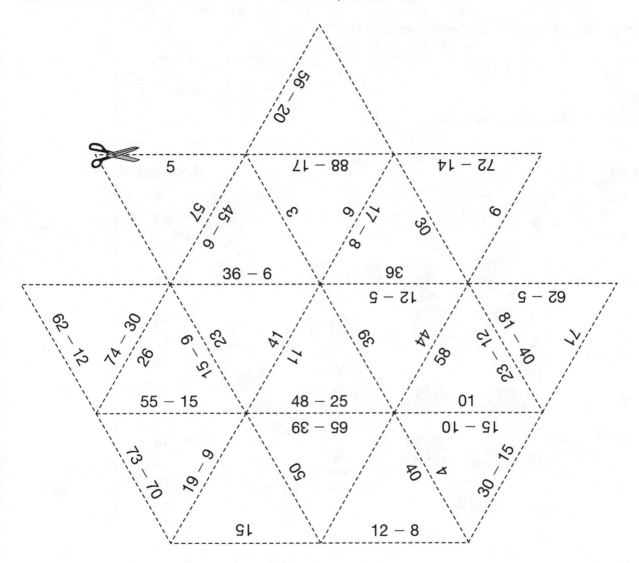

Multiplication Practice

Use a ruler to draw a line from each question to the correct answer.
Each line will cross a letter and a number. The number tells you where
to put the letter to solve the riddle.

Riddle: What has 24 legs and moves across ice?

1	2	3

4	5	6	7	8	9
		C			

10	11	12	13	14

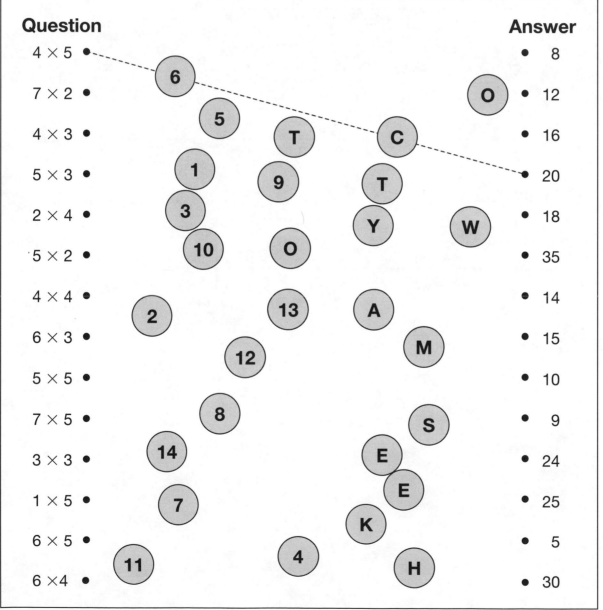

Question		Answer
4 × 5		8
7 × 2		12
4 × 3		16
5 × 3		20
2 × 4		18
5 × 2		35
4 × 4		14
6 × 3		15
5 × 5		10
7 × 5		9
3 × 3		24
1 × 5		25
6 × 5		5
6 × 4		30

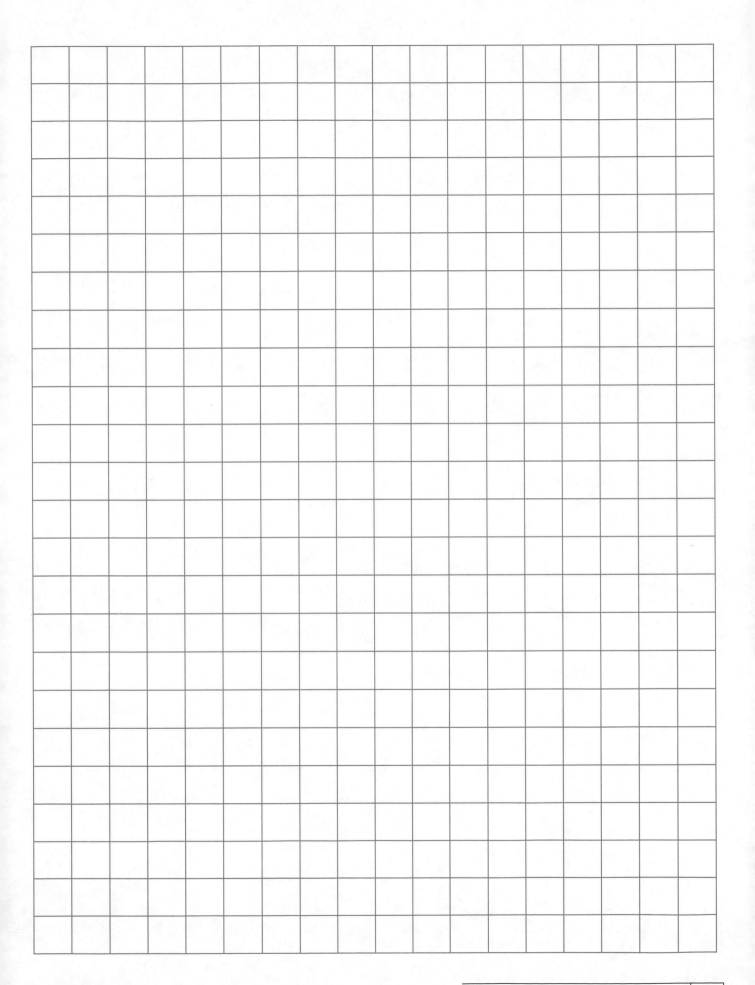

Triangle Dot Paper

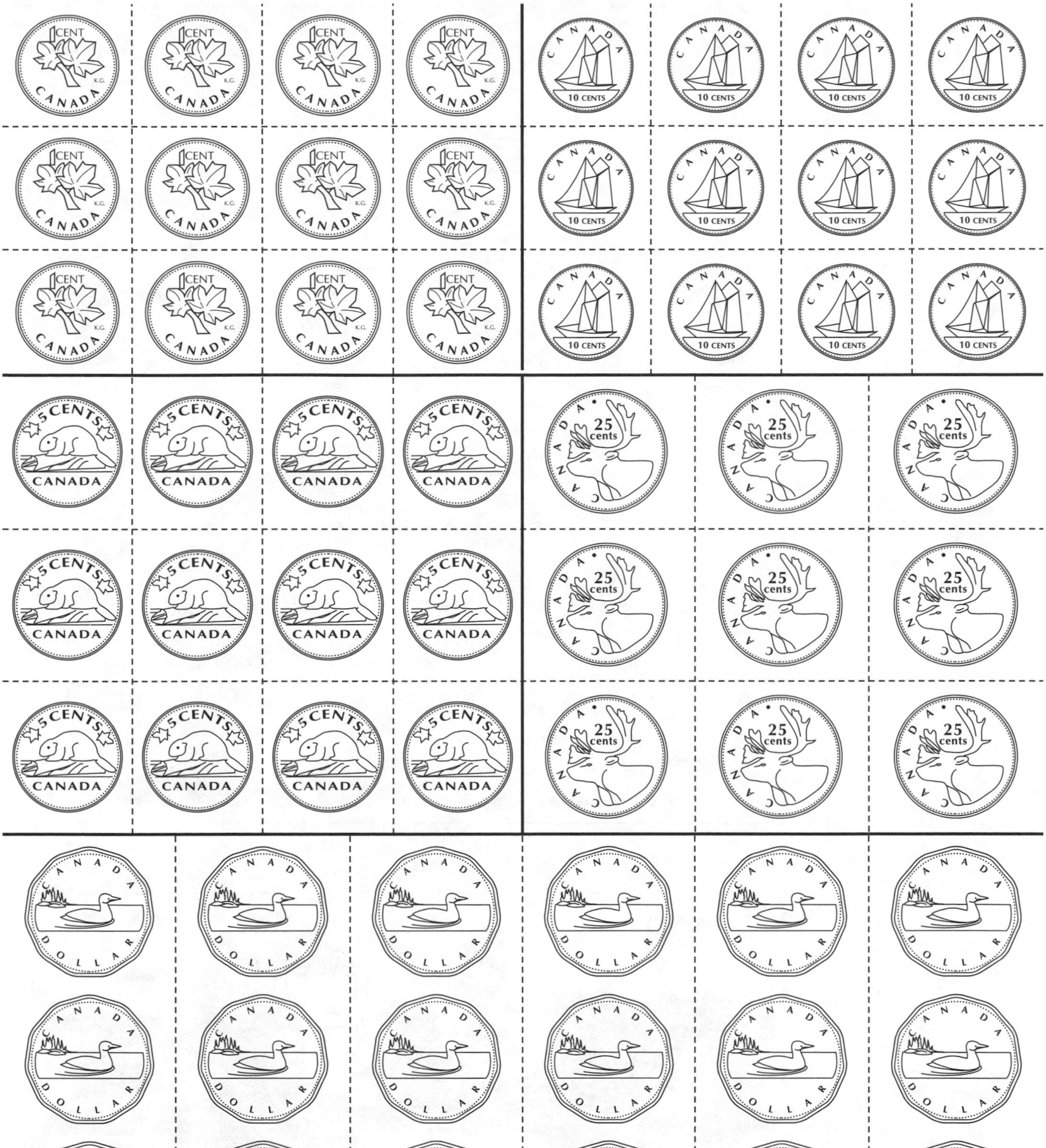
CENT
CANADA
10 CENTS
5 CENTS
25 cents
DOLLAR

1	2	3	4	5	6	7	8	9	10
11	12	13	14	15	16	17	18	19	20
21	22	23	24	25	26	27	28	29	30
31	32	33	34	35	36	37	38	39	40
41	42	43	44	45	46	47	48	49	50
51	52	53	54	55	56	57	58	59	60
61	62	63	64	65	66	67	68	69	70
71	72	73	74	75	76	77	78	79	80
81	82	83	84	85	86	87	88	89	90
91	92	93	94	95	96	97	98	99	100

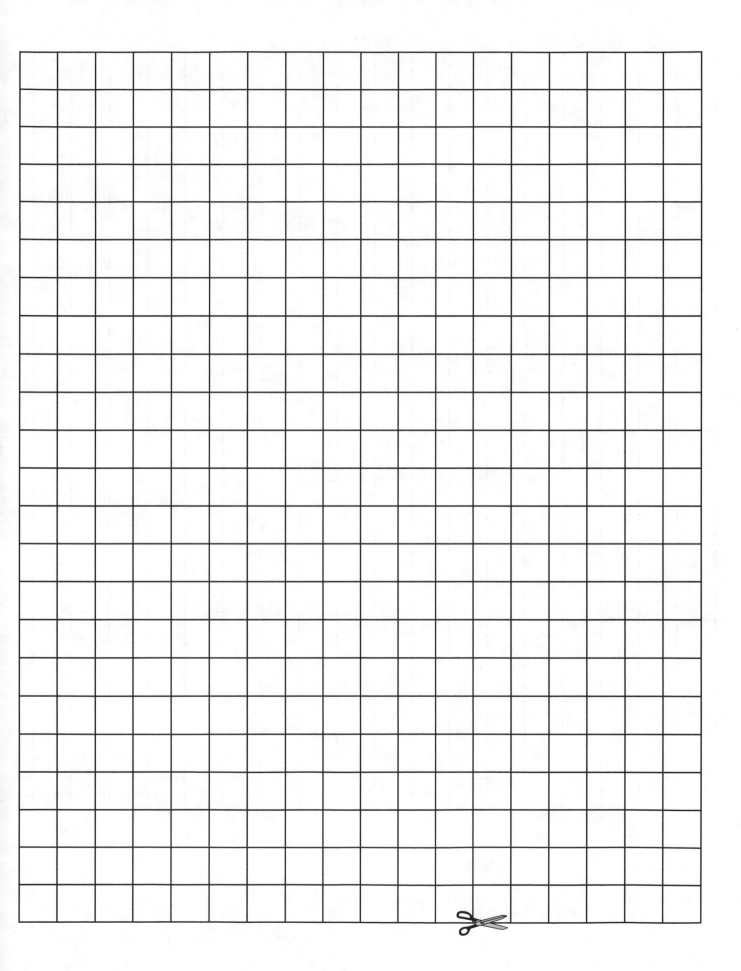

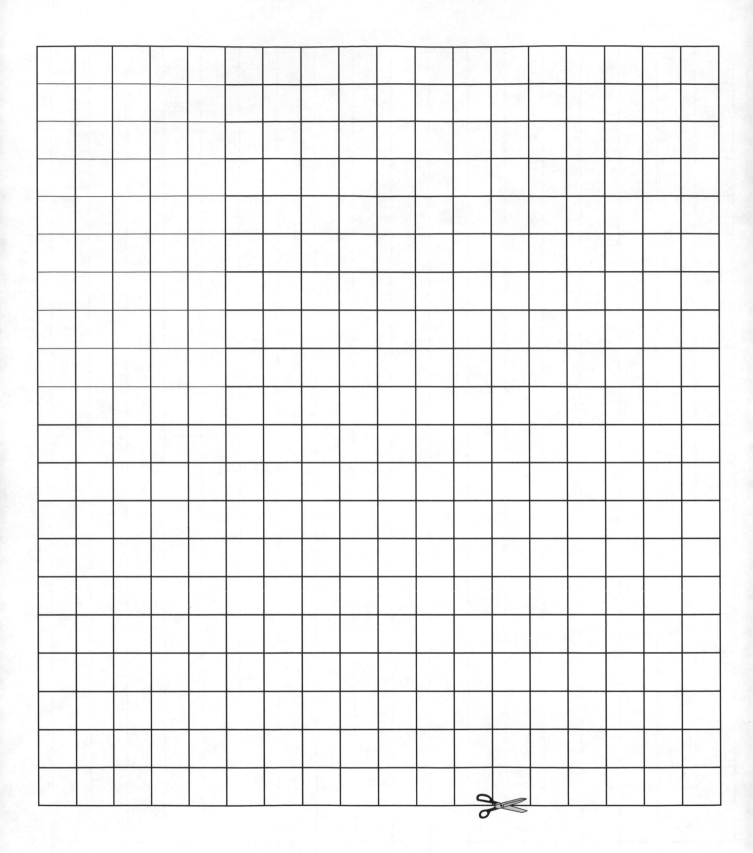

Thousands	Hundreds	Tens	Ones

Ones

Tens

Hundreds

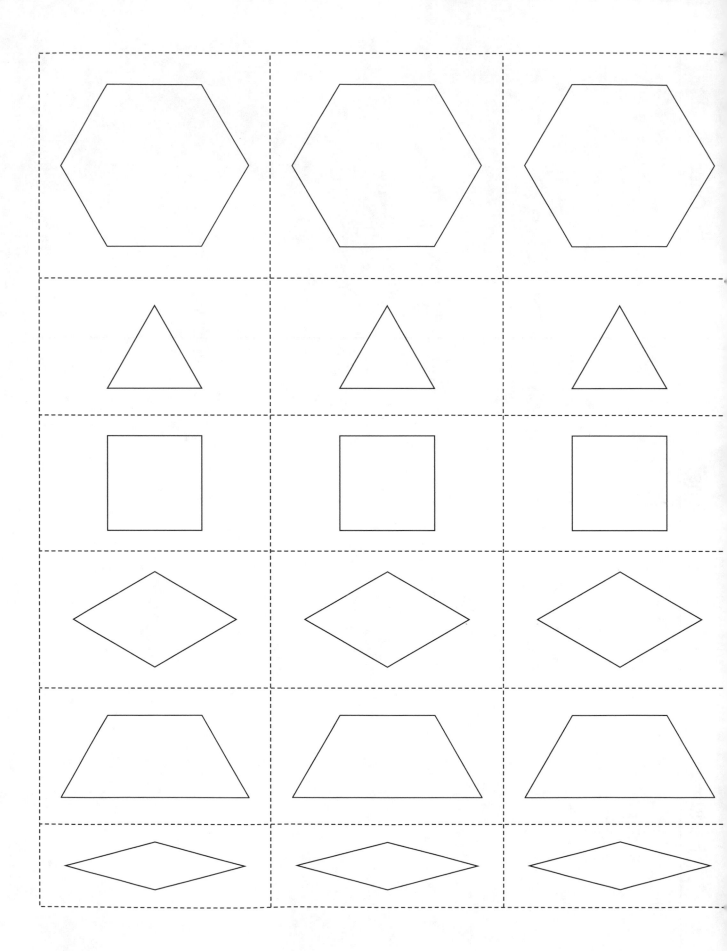

Pattern Block Shapes